Hook 'Em While You Can

By: Dr. Deborah Bowie

Illustrated by: Marlysse Hall

"I hate writing!

Why do I need to learn how to write a story anyway?

It's not like I want to be an author when I grow up."

These were the resounding words of Daryan

as the teacher called all the students to the rug.

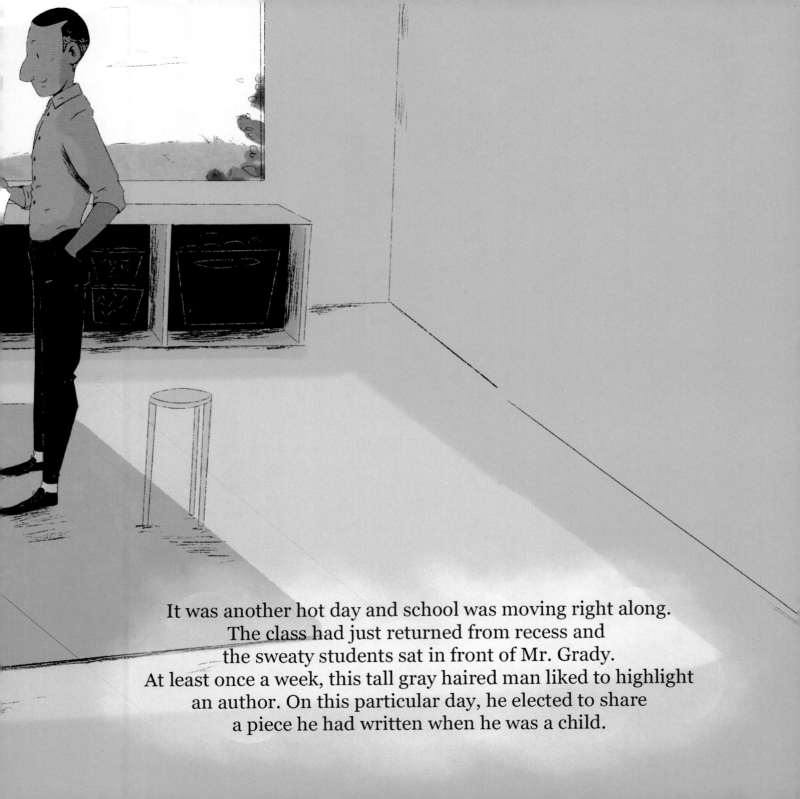

It was another hot day and school was moving right along.
The class had just returned from recess and
the sweaty students sat in front of Mr. Grady.
At least once a week, this tall gray haired man liked to highlight
an author. On this particular day, he elected to share
a piece he had written when he was a child.

Mr. Grady started reading, "This is a story about a boy named Tony."

"He was the oldest boy in the family."

"He went to see
his Grandma in Mississippi.
Tony loved his Grandma.

Tony..."

"Mr. Grady, that story is boring!"
Daryan was a child who always spoke his mind.

"What do you mean it's boring?" Mr. Grady inquired.

Daryan answered very matter-of-factly,
"Mr. G. aren't you the one who told us
that our writing should grab
the reader in the beginning?"

Mr. Grady nodded in agreement.
"You didn't make me want to hear
anymore with that opening."
The other children chimed in
with their comments and approval
of Daryan's words.

Interested in where this conversation was going,

Mr. Grady pursued. "But it gets better later...really!"

One of the other students added,
"Mr. Grady, if we can't get past the first paragraph,
how will we ever know if the rest of the story is good or not?"

Another student pressed further with,
"Yeah! I mean, we have different rules and stuff
for picking books that are on our level.
If we're already limited by that,
I don't want to waste time with a book that may or
may not improve by the end of the first page!"

A smile crossed Mr. Grady's face as he affirmed
the arguments presented by the students.
"You're right! I knew I had the smartest class.
There's just one more problem...."

"What's that?"
Daryan questioned with great curiosity.

"I was sitting at home last night, eager to read these
wonderful stories...

...When all of a sudden I got really,
really, tired."

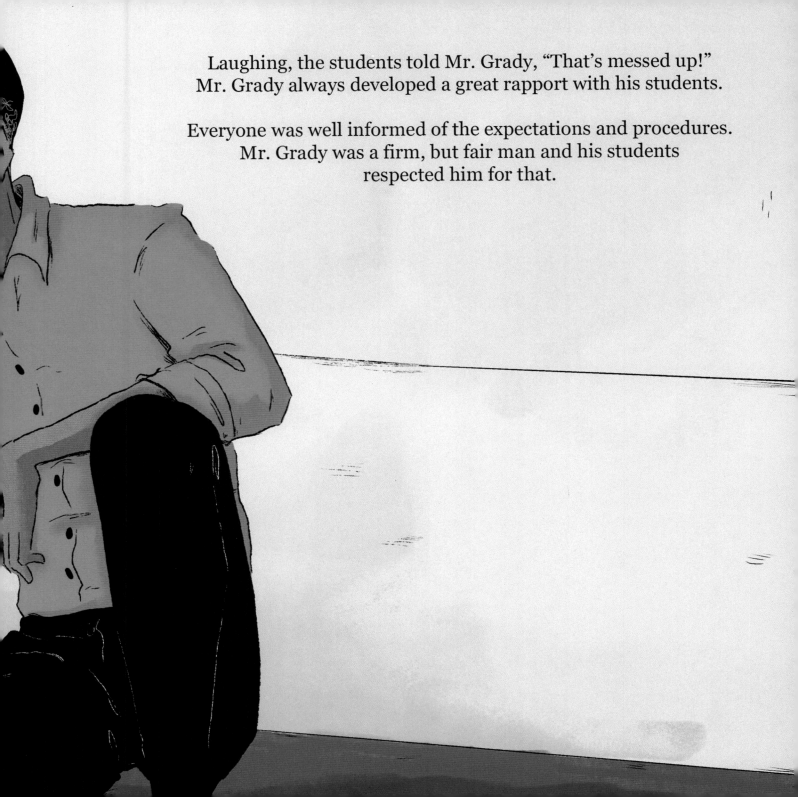

Laughing, the students told Mr. Grady, "That's messed up!"
Mr. Grady always developed a great rapport with his students.

Everyone was well informed of the expectations and procedures.
Mr. Grady was a firm, but fair man and his students
respected him for that.

Mr. Grady continued the conversation. "To help myself stay awake till at least nine o' clock, I decided to do some math."

"Math?!?" the students exclaimed.

"Remember when we talked about tally marks?" asked Mr. Grady

"Yes sir."

"Well, I made a chart that looks like this."
He showed the students a blank chart
with columns and titles that said:
Great, Okay, and Snore.

The students were inquisitive. They wondered
where Mr. Grady was going with this.

"Then I made another one that showed
how each of your stories started." He pulled out another chart
with two columns this time. The students were amazed to see that thirteen
of the nineteen students had started their story in the exact same way
they said was boring when Mr. Grady did it.

Daryan sat silently as he knew he was one of the thirteen.

Mr. Grady was pleased with their reaction because he knew some of them were really thinking about what they had talked about.

For the rest of them, he explained what had just happened.

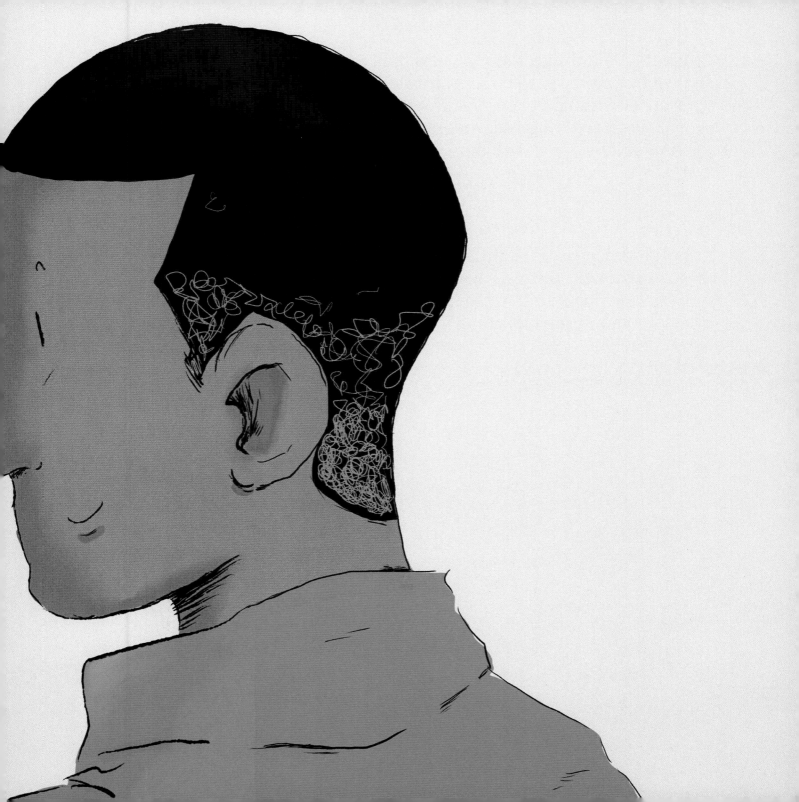

"Students, I did things the way I did today because I wanted you to be responsible for your own learning. For the last few days, I have been teaching you this concept, but too many of you still didn't get it.

I was starting to get a little frustrated because I thought this was an easy concept. I was teaching it, but for some reason, you weren't learning it.

Then I realized, you have to get it for yourself to be able to really know what we're talking about.

Do you understand what I'm saying?"

The children nodded.

"I **do** want to share the beginning of Henry's story if that's okay with him."

Henry shrugged and nodded as if to say, "*I don't care, just don't make me read it.*"

Mr. Grady started off.
"Don't let her slip!"

"Everyone was staring at the top of the tree
where the cat had gotten stuck in a limb
where most people were scared to climb.
Katherine had just reached the
very important branch."

"How many of you are interested in the rest of the story?"

Every hand shot up.

"Well, you'll have to wait until Henry is finished and ready to publish his final piece." Awweee's rang throughout the classroom. "I do have to say though, that is one of the best pieces of writing I've read so far this year. I could visualize everything that was happening as Henry described it. Job well done, Henry. I look forward to reading great things from all of you."

Henry shyly put his head down and smiled to himself.

Mr. Grady told the students that they were to return to their seats and either start a new piece or improve the one they already started.

As he walked around the room, Mr. Grady glanced over the shoulders of the students to see if they had taken heed to their own advice. He had a clipboard with the words: Great, Okay, and Snore at the top of each column.

He was pleased with what he saw.

THE END

READING SKILLS:

Vocabulary	Instead of SAID
resounding	inquired
affirmed	answered
eager	pursued
rapport	added
inquisitive	told
heed	exclaimed
	questioned
	asked
	interjected

Activity

Students could practice writing "hooks" to some of their favorite stories.

Students may write the rest of Henry's story how they would imagine it ends.

"Don't let her slip! Everyone was staring at the top of the tree where the cat had gotten stuck in a limb where most people were scared to climb. Katherine had just reached the very important branch."